by Jules Feiffer

McGraw-Hill Book Company, Inc.

New York Toronto London

About Jules Feiffer

There's a story about an adolescent boy who was taken to a psychiatrist. The doctor drew a rectangle on a sheet of paper and showed it to the boy. "What does it make you think of?" he asked. The boy looked at it and said, "Sex." The doctor got the same response when he drew a circle on the paper. When he had drawn a triangle and an octagon and an ellipse with the same results, he said, "Son, you need help." The boy was amazed. "But, doc," he protested, *"you're* the one that's drawing the dirty pictures."

Jules Feiffer, too, draws things on sheets of paper and lets us look at them. They mean different things to different people. When I saw my first Feiffer cartoon — dug from the wallet of a pioneer Feiffer-phile who had clipped it from *The Village Voice*—I almost fell out of my chair and rolled around on the floor of a painfully sedate East Fifties restaurant. The next Feiffer I saw was at a ferociously gay cocktail party; again it was taken from a wallet. This time, though, its effect was to make me so gloomy that I went right home and went to bed.

It was about this time that I became aware of a hard-core group of dedicated Feiffer-lovers. All of them carried Feiffer cartoons in their wallets, and the more advanced among them had long since discarded their driver's licenses, Austin-Healey registration papers, Museum of Modern Art membership cards, Diners' Club credentials and snapshots of their children in order to make more room for Feiffer clippings.

Some of these Feifferites were (and still are, I'll bet) rather odd sorts. One, an aggressively successful businessman, once turned up at a Beaux Arts Costume Ball dressed as a payroll—in order, he explained, to be able to introduce himself to a lot of bohemians who had never before been forced to meet one. Another, an attorney, is the compiler of a musical anthology called *Songs for Management,* of which the only number I recall is a ballad entitled "I Dreamed I Saw John D. Last Night, Alive as You or Me." Though they vary in politics, personality and profession, all Feifferites have one thing in common: they are deeply moved by Feiffer cartoons—not invariably, of course, but often enough to make them aware that Feiffer has Got Their Number and is Getting Through to Them. Some of them are moved toward giggles and some are moved toward guffaws; some are moved toward a nervous breakdown and some toward the nearest saloon; and a middle-aged schoolteacher in Stamford, Connecticut, says she gets a severe attack of the hiccups every time she sees a Feiffer strip.

Feiffer, incidentally, was born in Manhattan and, by nature a wanderer, has since lived in Brooklyn and the Bronx. He attended art classes at Pratt Institute before serving a hitch in the army, where he was not exactly a misfit and not exactly a fit. About a year ago he began contributing "Sick, Sick, Sick" to *The Village Voice* as a regular feature; it immediately attracted a following, and today there are subscribers whose only interest in the publication, despite the generally high level of its journalism, is the few square inches devoted to Feiffer's work.

Well, now the drawings are in a book, and you may think this will let confirmed Feiffer fans restore their wallets to conventional uses—but not so. Or, at least, not permanently so. For as fast as new Feiffer strips appear (at the rate of one a week), they'll be clipped and kept until wallets bulge as in pre-book days.

It would be nice, wouldn't it, if the book turned out to be a best seller. After all, why should Feiffer's be the only wallet without a bulge in it?

ED ZERN

ELEVEN YEARS
OLD AND I
CAN'T PLAY
BASEBALL.

1.

WHERE DID THE
TIME GO?
WHAT HAVE
I DONE WITH
IT?

2.

ELEVEN YEARS — HUH —
THAT'S STILL NOT
VERY OLD. IT'S NOT
LIKE I WAS **THIRTEEN**.
I **STILL** CAN LEARN!

3.

I CAN **PRACTICE**!
LEARN ALL THE
ANGLES! MAYBE
TAKE A FEW EVENING
COURSES. WHY I'VE
GOT A WHOLE
LIFETIME AHEAD
OF ME!

4.

5.

6.

ELEVEN
YEARS...

ELEVEN
YEARS....

— SHOT TO HELL —

8.

I'M AN
ARTIST.

1.

BUT ITS NOT WHAT
I REALLY WANT
TO DO.

2.

WHAT I REALLY
WANT TO DO
IS BE A SHOE
SALESMAN.

3.

I KNOW WHAT YOU'RE
GOING TO SAY —
"DREAMER —
GET YOUR HEAD
OUT OF THE
CLOUDS!"

4.

ALL RIGHT,
BUT ITS
WHAT I
WANT TO
DO.

5.

INSTEAD I
HAVE TO GO
ON **PAINTING**
ALL DAY LONG.

6.

7.

THE WORLD SHOULD
MAKE A PLACE
FOR SHOE
SALESMEN.

8.

HAVEN'T YOU FINISHED THE PAGE YET?

1.

2.

3.

4.

BUT TODAY **WHO** LISTENS TO
HIS MOTHER! HE SAYS,
"I ONLY LIKE TO KNOW
THINGS FOR THE **FUN** OF IT"

"FOR THE FUN OF IT" HE SAYS
CAN YOU **IMAGINE**
READING A BOOK FOR
THE **FUN** OF IT?

5.

6.

SO WITHOUT TELLING....
I SENT HIS NAME IN TO
"21"
"$64,000
QUESTION"
"BIG SURPRISE"
"TIC TAC DOUGH"
AND
"NAME THAT TUNE,"

HE'LL
LEARN.

7.

8.

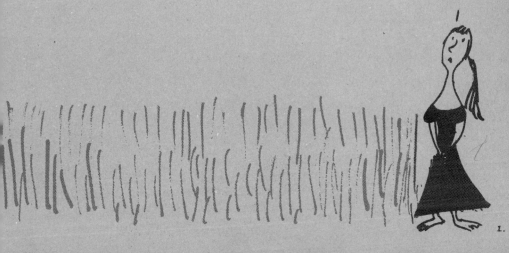

A
DANCE
TO
SPRING.

1.

3.

4.

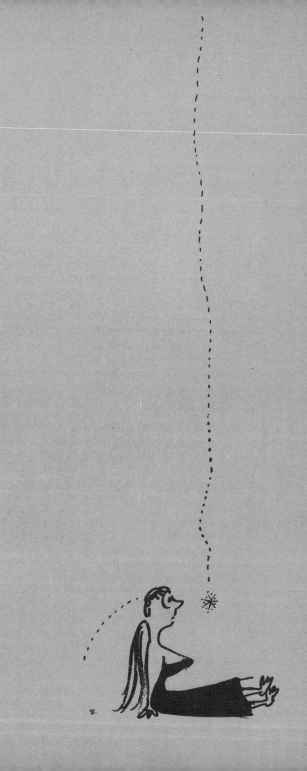

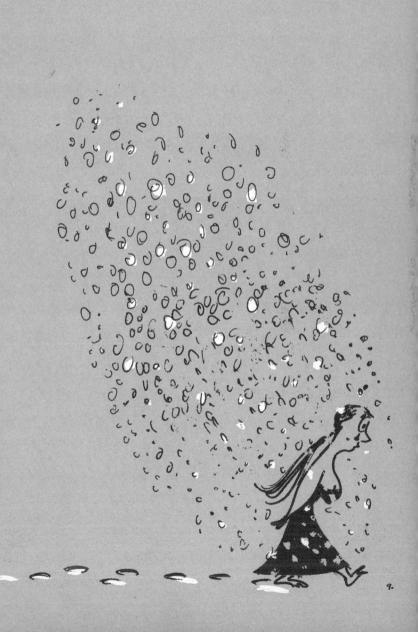

I KEEP
RUNNING
BUT I
DON'T
GET
ANYWHERE.

HI THERE HOWARD.

MURRAY'S
A GOOD EGG,
I SHOULD BE
GLAD TO SEE
HIM GET
AHEAD. I
WON'T BE
BITTER.

HELLO AND GOODBYE —
HOWARD.

LUCILLE HAS **LOOKS**.
NO WONDER SHE GETS AHEAD.
I BET SHE USES HER **BODY**.
BUT I WON'T BE BITTER.

*WATCH MY SPEED,
HOWARD.*

IRWIN IS FIVE YEARS
YOUNGER THAN ME
AND A NO GOOD PUNK!

I KNOW
I'D DO
BETTER
IF NOT
FOR THESE
STOMACH
ACHES.

MOST LAY LISTENERS
HOLD THE IMPRESSION
THAT OUR MODERN
JAZZ IDIOM STEMS
FROM THE FUSION
OF AFRICAN AND
NATIVE AMERICAN
RHYTHMS.

1.

NOTHING
COULD BE
FURTHER
FROM THE
TRUTH.

2.

JAZZ WAS
REALLY
INVENTED BY
STEVE ALLEN
IN 1955.

3.

ALLEN, ORIGINALLY
A BACHIAN SCHOLAR,
RECORDED THE
FIRST JAZZ
COMPOSITION IN
JUNE '55 ON THE
BRUNSWICK
LABEL.

4.

HE USED THE
PSEUDONYM
"JELLYROLL"
AND MAINTAINED
HIS ANONYMITY
UNTIL THE
PUBLIC ACCEPTED
JAZZ AS THE
NEWEST OF
FOLK ARTS.

5.

SINCE THEN JAZZ
HAS **SWEPT** THE
NATION. SUCH SONGS
AS *"YOU AIN'T
NOTHIN' BUT A
HOUND DOG"* AND
*"THROW MAMMA FROM
THE TRAIN A KISS,
A KISS"* HAVE
BECOME PART OF
EVERY AMERICAN'S
VOCABULARY.

6.

WE EVEN
TEACH
ABOUT IT
AT THE
NEW
SCHOOL.

7.

IF YOU DON'T
LIKE IT
**YOU'D BETTER
LEARN.** IT'S
THE COMING
THING.

8.

I **USED** TO BE A REBEL IN MY YOUTH.

1.

THIS CAUSE...
THAT CAUSE...
(CHUCKLE) I BACKED 'EM **ALL**.

2.

BUT I LEARNED.

3.

REBELLION IS SIMPLY A **DEVICE** USED BY THE IMMATURE TO **HIDE** FROM HIS OWN PROBLEMS.

4.

SO I LOST INTEREST IN POLITICS.

5.

NOW WHEN I FEEL AROUSED
BY A **CIVIL RIGHTS** CASE
OR A **PASSPORT** HEARING....

6.

I **REALIZE** IT'S
JUST A DEVICE.

7.

I GO TO MY ANALYST
AND WE WORK IT OUT.

8.

YOU HAVE NO IDEA HOW
MUCH **BETTER** I FEEL
THESE DAYS.

9.

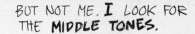

SOME PEOPLE SEE **EVERYTHING** IN TERMS OF BLACK AND WHITE.

BUT NOT ME. **I** LOOK FOR THE **MIDDLE TONES.**

1.

2.

LIKE MOST GIRLS IF THEIR BLIND DATE LEAVES THEM IN A RESTAURANT TO MAKE A PHONE CALL AND HE DOESN'T COME BACK... THEY'D SEE THAT IN TERMS OF BLACK AND WHITE.

BUT NOT ME. **I** LOOK FOR **MOTIVATION.**

3.

4.

LIKE,.... COMPULSIVE SOCIAL BEHAVIOR PATTERNS..

OR ERRATIC INTERPERSONAL ADJUSTMENTS

OR HOSTILE GROUP ATTITUDES

5.

THERE MUST BE SOME **BASIC** DRIVE THAT MAKES HIM FLEE FROM A BLIND DATE.

6.

SO WHY GET UPSET? IT HAS **NOTHING** TO DO WITH **ME** PERSONALLY.

7.

I HOPE HE WORKS IT OUT SOON. I'M GETTING TIRED OF WAITING.

8.

COME OVER HERE
AND KISS YOUR
AUNT PEGGY
GOODBYE!

I SWEAR, PEGGY— HIM AND
HIS LITTLE BROTHER—
IT'S LIKE **DAY AND NIGHT**.

SEE HOW NICE YOUR
LITTLE BROTHER HUGS
YOUR AUNT PEGGY?

ONE IS GOOD AS GOLD.
THE OTHER IS NOTHING BUT
TROUBLE. **ARE YOU**
COMING OVER HERE?

ISN'T THAT A GEM? LOOK HOW
THE LITTLE ONE LAUGHS
EVERYTIME I YELL AT HIS
BIG BROTHER. HE'S **ALWAYS**
HAPPY.

SEE HOW YOUR LITTLE
BROTHER IS LAUGHING
AT YOU?

YOU'RE NOT HERE IN
ONE SECOND FLAT
I'LL SMACK YOU AND **THEN**
WATCH HIM LAUGH.

my leg
hurts

(CHUCKLE) HIS LEG
ALWAYS HURTS WHEN
I YELL AT HIM.

I SWEAR, PEGGY,
SOMETIMES KIDS
ARE BEYOND ME.

I'M **ALWAYS** HAVING A GOOD TIME.

1.

MOST PEOPLE **HATE** THEIR JOBS. I'VE BEEN HERE **FIFTEEN** YEARS.

2.

LOVED **EVERY** MINUTE OF IT.

3.

SEEN BOSSES COME — SEEN BOSSES GO. I **JOKED** WITH 'EM ALL.

4.

THAT'S BECAUSE I KNOW HOW TO GET ALONG.

5.

I KID THE
OFFICE STAFF.
TELL 'EM GAGS
ON THE BOSS..

THEY EAT
IT UP.

6.

7.

BUT THEN I
COOPERATE
WITH THE
BOSS **TOO**.

... LIKE I TELL HIM WHO
COMES IN LATE AND
WHO SPENDS TIME
IN THE WASHROOM...

8.

9.

THEY CALL
ME MR.
SUNSHINE.

10.

1. THE ITEM ON THE AGENDA, GENTLEMEN, IS THE **FALLOUT** BIT. OUR CLIENT ISN'T HAPPY WITH OUR CAMPAIGN.

2. THE PUBLIC IS **NEGATIVE** FALL OUT CONSCIOUS. WE MUST MAKE THEM **POSITIVE** FALLOUT CONSCIOUS.

3. I HAVE HERE THE OUTLINE OF A "FALLOUT IS GOOD FOR YOU" SATURATION CAMPAIGN.

4. IT INCLUDES SUCH ITEMS AS "I LIKE FALLOUT" BUTTONS, DECALS INSCRIBED WITH "YOUR GOVERNMENT KNOWS BEST" — A TV SPEC CALLED "I FELL FOR FALLOUT"

AND AS A CAPPER - A "MR. AND MRS. MUTATION" CONTEST- DESIGNED TO CHANGE THE CONCEPT OF **BEAUTY** IN THE AMERICAN MIND.

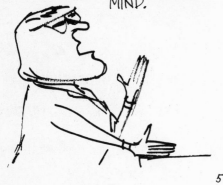

5.

BUT WHAT ABOUT THE **SCIENTISTS**, CHIEF?

6.

NO PROBLEM. WE'LL SAY THEY'RE "**ORGANIZED**" AND HAVE THEM ALL SUBPOENAED.

7.

IT'S ONE OF OUR MOST SUCCESSFUL SALES DEVICES.

8.

WELCOME
BACK FOR
YOUR
13th
CONSECUTIVE
WEEK,
EVELYN.

THANK
YOU,
RED.

1.

EVELYN, WILL YOU GO INTO THE
AUTO-SUGGESTION BOOTH AND
TAKE YOUR REGULAR PLACE
ON THE PSYCHO-PROMPTER
COUCH?

THANK
YOU,
RED.

2.

NOW, EVELYN, LAST WEEK YOU
WENT UP TO $40,000 BY PROPERLY
CITING YOUR RIVALRY WITH
YOUR SIBLING AS A COMPULSIVE
SADO-MASOCHISTIC BEHAVIOR
PATTERN WHICH DEVELOPED OUT OF
AN EARLY POST-NATAL FEEDING
PROBLEM.

YES,
RED.

3.

BUT— LATER, WHEN ASKED
ABOUT PRE-ADOLESCENT
OEDIPAL PHANTASY
REPRESSIONS, YOU
RATIONALIZED TWICE
AND **MENTAL BLOCKED**
THREE TIMES.

4.

NOW AT $300 PER
RATIONALIZATION AND
$500 PER MENTAL
BLOCK YOU **LOST**
$2,100 OFF YOUR
$40,000 LEAVING YOU
WITH A TOTAL OF
$37,900!

YES,
RED

5.

NOW, **ANY** COMBINATION OF **TWO** MORE
MENTAL BLOCKS AND **EITHER ONE**
RATIONALIZATION OR **THREE** DEFENSIVE
PROJECTIONS WILL PUT YOU **OUT OF
THE GAME.** ARE YOU WILLING
TO GO AHEAD?

YES,
RED.

6.

I MIGHT SAY HERE THAT
ALL OF EVELYN'S
QUESTIONS AND ANSWERS
HAVE BEEN CHECKED FOR
ACCURACY WITH HER
ANALYST. ,

7.

NOW EVELYN, FOR $80,000
EXPLAIN THE FAILURE OF
YOUR THREE MARRIAGES.

WELL
I —

8.

WE'LL GET BACK TO
EVELYN IN **ONE**
MINUTE. **FIRST** A
WORD ABOUT OUR
PRODUCT.

9.

NOW LET
ME MAKE
MYSELF
CLEAR.

1.

NOW WE HAVE A LAW AND WE
ARE A COUNTRY GOVERNED BY
LAW. I WANT YOU TO KNOW
I FEEL **STRONGLY** ABOUT
THAT.

2.

NOW THERE ARE LAWS WE LIKE
AND LAWS WE DON'T LIKE. BUT—
AND I WANT TO MAKE THIS
CLEAR— WE MUST **OBEY** OUR
LAWS OR ELSE
WE COULD AID
COMMUNISM.

3.

NOW HERE IS THE
LAW OF THE LAND.
AND THAT IS THAT
AND WE MUST
ENFORCE IT.

4.

NOW THE REST OF THE WORLD IS WATCHING— LET ME MAKE THAT CLEAR— AND WHETHER WE LIKE IT OR NOT— LOTS OF THEM ARE **COLORED**.

5.

BUT THAT'S **NATURE'S** LAW AND WE MUST LIVE WITH IT. I CAN'T STRESS THAT TOO FIRMLY.

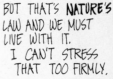

6.

NOW LET'S PULL TOGETHER **VOLUNTARILY** AND THAT WILL SOLVE IT ALL AND WHETHER WE LIKE IT OR NOT—FORGE AHEAD.

7.

AND THE REST OF THE WORLD WILL RESPECT US FOR OUR MORAL STAND.

8.

IT STARTED
WITH MY
MOTHER.

SHE SAID:
"YOU **ALWAYS**
HAVE TO BE
DIFFERENT.
WHY DON'T YOU
GO OUT AND
PLAY LIKE
EVERYONE
ELSE?"

SO I DID. AND
I MADE FRIENDS.
AND MY
FRIENDS
SAID:

"YOU **ALWAYS**
HAVE TO BE
DIFFERENT.
WHY DON'T
YOU JOIN
GANGS
LIKE
EVERYONE
ELSE?"

SO I DID. AND THINGS WERE GOING ALONG **FINE**.

UNTIL COLLEGE WHEN MY ADVISER SAID: "DON'T BE **SOCIALLY HOSTILE**. JOIN A FRAT LIKE EVERYONE ELSE."

SO I DID. AND I BOUGHT A PIPE — AND I STARTED BOOZING — AND SOON YOU COULDN'T TELL ME FROM EVERYONE ELSE.

SO WHEN I GOT OUT, I JOINED MADISON AVENUE.

NOW THEY TELL ME I'M A CONFORMIST.

WE WANT YOU TO FEEL HAPPY ON THE JOB, HOWARD—AND A MAN WHO **STRIDES** IN HERE AND **DEMANDS** MORE MONEY— WELL, THAT'S NOT A HAPPY MAN, HOWARD.

5.

NOW, PERHAPS YOU'D BE HAPPIER SOMEWHERE ELSE.

6.

BUT THAT'S **YOUR** DECISION TO MAKE, FELLA. TAKE **ALL** THE TIME YOU LIKE.

7.

I'LL JUST GO ON SIGNING THESE PAPERS.

8.

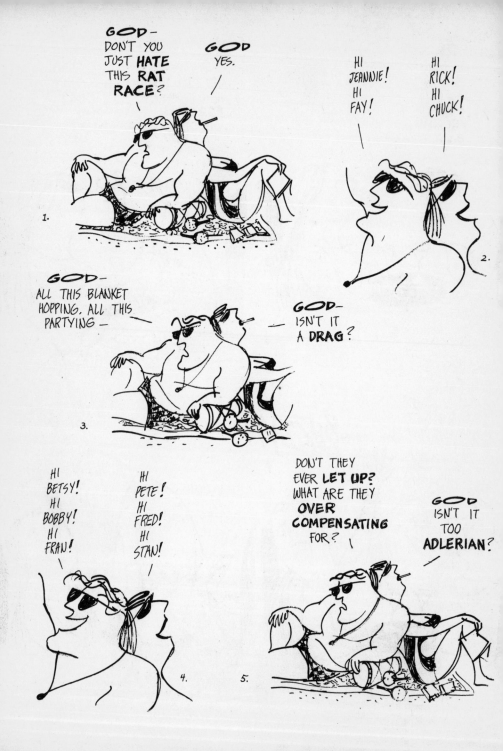

HI FRITZI!
HI ROZ! HI
CANDY! HI BEV!
HI GIGI!
HI DOT!

HI ROCK! HI
DEAN! HI BUZZ!
HI LEE! HI
RED! HI
BILLIE!

6.

HOW I'LL **EVER**
GET THROUGH
LABOR DAY IS
BEYOND ME.
HOW OFTEN DO
YOU COME OUT?

EVERY
WEEKEND

7.

HI FLO! HI GAIL!
HI LILA! HI JANE!
HI DORIS! HI SUE!
HI MAY! HI PEG!
HI EVE!

HI GRANT! HI JER!
HI BUDDY! HI PHIL!
HI NEIL! HI LOU!
HI SPENCE! HI TIGE!
HI RON!

8.

THEY LEAD
SUCH
EMPTY
LIVES.

HI CASEY! HI MARK!
HI TOBY! HI FRANZ!
HI SAL! HI KENT!
HI ANDRE'!
HI NAT----

9.

ELEVEN
YEARS
OLD AND
I'M
NEVER
PICKED
FOR THE
TEAM.

1.

LOOK AT
THOSE
OTHERS.
THEY
ALWAYS
PLAY.

2.

BATTING THE
BALL ...
CATCHING IT.

3.

RUNNING...
LAUGHING...

4.

5.

THERE'S
SOMETHING
BASICALLY
WRONG
THERE.

6.

SOMETHING **BAD.** SOMETHING **UNHEALTHY.**

THE WAY THEY
GATHER
TOGETHER.
THE WAY THEY
CHOOSE
UP SIDES.

8.

IT'S VERY
LUCKY THEY
WON'T LET
ME PLAY.

9.

OTHERWISE
I MIGHT
NOT HAVE
NOTICED.

MAN, THAT'S
WHAT A
REBEL **IS.**

1.

I MEAN HE DON'T
TALK UP TO NO
JUDGE. HE DON'T
SAY IT'S A **BAD
RAP.**

2.

'CAUSE HE **KNOWS** HE'S
GUILTY. LIKE TO HIM
JUST **LIVING** IS A
CRIME.

3.

SO HE **CUTS OUT-**
YOU KNOW, MAN —
HE **WITHDRAWS.**

4.

AND HE GOES WITH HIS **OWN** AND HE SAYS, "**SQUARES** I DO NOT **KNOW** YOU." THAT'S **REBELLION** MAN.

5.

AND HE LEARNS A **NEW** TONGUE - LIKE A **DIFFERENT LANGUAGE** - AND WHEN THE SQUARES COME AROUND, HE SAYS "**WHAT** ARE THEY SAYING?" THAT'S **REBELLION** MAN.

6.

AND SOON HE'S **SO** WITHDRAWN HE ONLY HEARS **HIMSELF**. SO HE WRITES IT IN A BOOK.

7.

AND THE SQUARES SAY, "**HEY** - HERE'S THE **LATEST!** "

8.

SO THEY **BUY** HIS WITHDRAWAL AND EVERYONE MAKES A **MINT**.

9.

THAT'S REBELLION, MAN.

10.

ALL RIGHT NOW — ALL AT ONCE — WHO'S AWARE?

1.

WE'RE AWARE

WHAT'S THE PASSWORD?

2.

3.

ORGANIZATION MAN!

THAT'S THE OLD PASSWORD.

4.

5.

THAT WAS ON LAST YEARS BOOK LIST. WHAT'S THE **NEW** PASSWORD?

6.

IN GROUP? OUTGROUP? CONFORMIST?

7.

LATENT?
MATERIALISTIC?
MATRIARCHAL?
HOW ABOUT ORWELLIAN—? THAT'S ALWAYS SAFE.

8.

HE'S NOT AWARE!

9

NOW THEN, WHAT'S THE PASSWORD?

MOTIVATIONAL RESEARCH

10.

GOOD— WITHOUT THE LATEST PASSWORD WE'D NEVER KNOW WHAT'S WRONG WITH US.

11.

THE **FIRST** ONE
WE BUILT WAS
RELATIVELY
THIS SMALL.

BUT IT
HAD **THIS**
MUCH
FALLOUT-

BUT IN **THOSE**
DAYS FALLOUT
WAS NOT YET
A FAD. SO WE
IGNORED IT.

THE NEXT ONE
WE BUILT WAS
THIS BIG.

BUT IT HAD
THIS MUCH
FALLOUT.

OF COURSE **NONE** OF
US FELT GOOD ABOUT IT.
MY WIFE AND I **DOUBLED**
OUR DONATION TO OUR
REGULAR CHARITIES.

IT'S UP THERE ALLRIGHT. I CAN ALMOST SEE IT.

BLINKING..

TWINKLING..

STOP MOCKING US YOU RASCAL!

1.

2.

3.

I WON'T **THINK** OF IT. IF I DON'T THINK OF IT MAYBE IT'LL GO AWAY — I'LL THINK OF **OTHER** THINGS... **AMERICAN** THINGS...

MIKE TODD...

QUEEN ELIZABETH...

STILL UP THERE ALL RIGHT.

4.

5.

6.

PROBABLY WON'T LAST THE NIGHT—PROBABLY CRUMBLE AND FALL— WHAT'D **THEY** EVER INVENT THAT WAS ANY GOOD?

7.

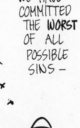

8.

BLAST IT OUT OF THE SKY I SAY!

9.

WHAT'S THE USE—? WHAT'S THE SENSE IN GOING ON—?

crack

10.

WE HAVE COMMITTED THE **WORST** OF ALL POSSIBLE SINS—

11.

WE WERE SECOND.

12.

SO I
QUIT THE
SECOND
GROUP AND
LOST ALL
THE FRIENDS
I HAD MADE.

AND I JOINED UP
WITH THIS **NEW**
GROUP. I
FOUGHT LIKE
HELL FOR
THEM.

5.

TILL THIS ONE GUY
CAME ALONG AND
PROVED THAT
THERE WASN'T
ANY WORD AT ALL.
THAT I SHOULD
GO OFF AS
AN **INDIVIDUAL**
AND **GROW!**

6.

SO I QUIT
THE LAST
GROUP
AND LOST
ALL THE
FRIENDS
I HAD
MADE.

7.

AND NOW I SIT
HOME ALONE ALL
DAY AND
ALL I
DO IS
GROW.

8.

IT WOULD BE NICE
TO JOIN UP WITH
SOME
OTHERS
WHO
FEEL
THE
WAY
I DO.

9.

CAN'T YOU **SEE**
BERNARD?
IT'S **NO GOOD**.

YOU'RE A **DOLL** AND
I'M IN**SANE** ABOUT
YOU - BUT IT **REALLY**
WOULDN'T JELL,
BERNARD.

WE'RE **DIFFERENT!**
I'M JUST **MANIC**
FOR PARTIES - FOR
FUN PEOPLE - FOR
HAVING A **BALL**.

AND **YOU**
DIG
TELEVISION.

I WANT TO DANCE AND
FEEL **FREE** - TO GO
BACK TO MAJORCA AND
GAMBLE AND MAKE
LOVE

THE REPORTS
ARE ALL IN,
GENTLEMEN—
WE HAVE
RESEARCHED
ANGER
AND FOUND IT
MARKETABLE

1.

OUR NATION—
WIDE SURVEY
SHOWS A
GROWING
CONSUMER —
TREND
AGAINST
CONFORMITY.
A NEW
STRESS IS
BEING PLACED
UPON THE
INDIVIDUAL.

2.

ANGRY
YOUNG
MEN
ARE
THE
LITERARY
RAGE.

3.

BUT
LITERATURE
IS NOT
ENOUGH —
ANGER
MUST
RIDE
WITH THE
TIMES,
GENTLEMEN.

4.

WE MUST
MERCHANDISE
IT IN
USEFUL
WAYS—
KEEP IT
LOUD!
KEEP IT
HARMLESS!

5.

WE CAN HAVE
ANGRY
SPORTS CAR
RALLIES —
ANGRY
IVY LEAGUE
SUITS —
ANGRY
PUSH
BUTTON
SHAVES —

6.

"TAKE THE **THREAT** OUT OF ANGER *!* " IS OUR BATTLE CRY. OUR PRODUCT WILL BE A **FRIENDLY** ANGER – A NEEDED OUTLET – **HURTFUL** TO NO ONE –

ALREADY IN THE WORKS IS A RECORDING ON THE "FURY" LABEL ENTITLED " **PROFANITY IN HI FI** "

AND AS A START WE ARE PRINTING UP A SERIES OF ANGRY PETITIONS FOR SAFE CAUSES –

7.

8.

9.

THIS MUST BE THE **BANNER YEAR** FOR ANGER, GENTLEMEN – REMEMBER – ANGER CAN BE **SOLD***!*

NEXT YEAR WE CAN GO BACK TO TRANQUILIZERS.

10.

11.

COME IN AT 9:00 —
"HI PHIL —
HI RAY —
HI CHARLIE —"
TALK — READ
THE PAPERS —
IT'S 9:30 —

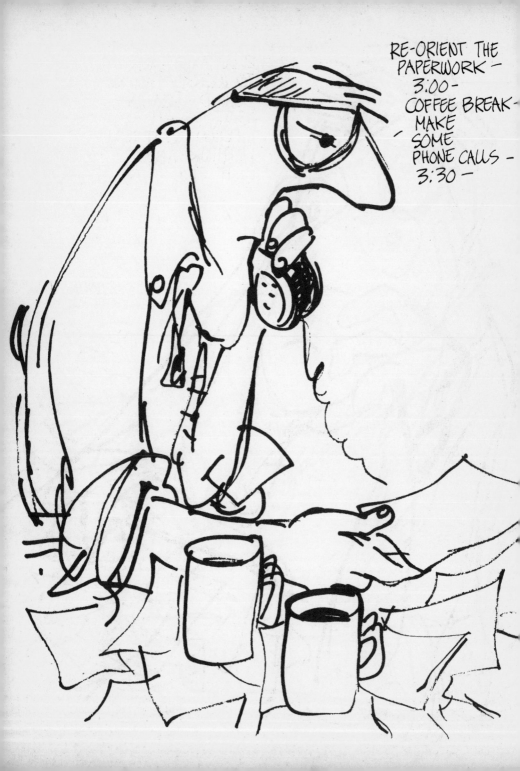

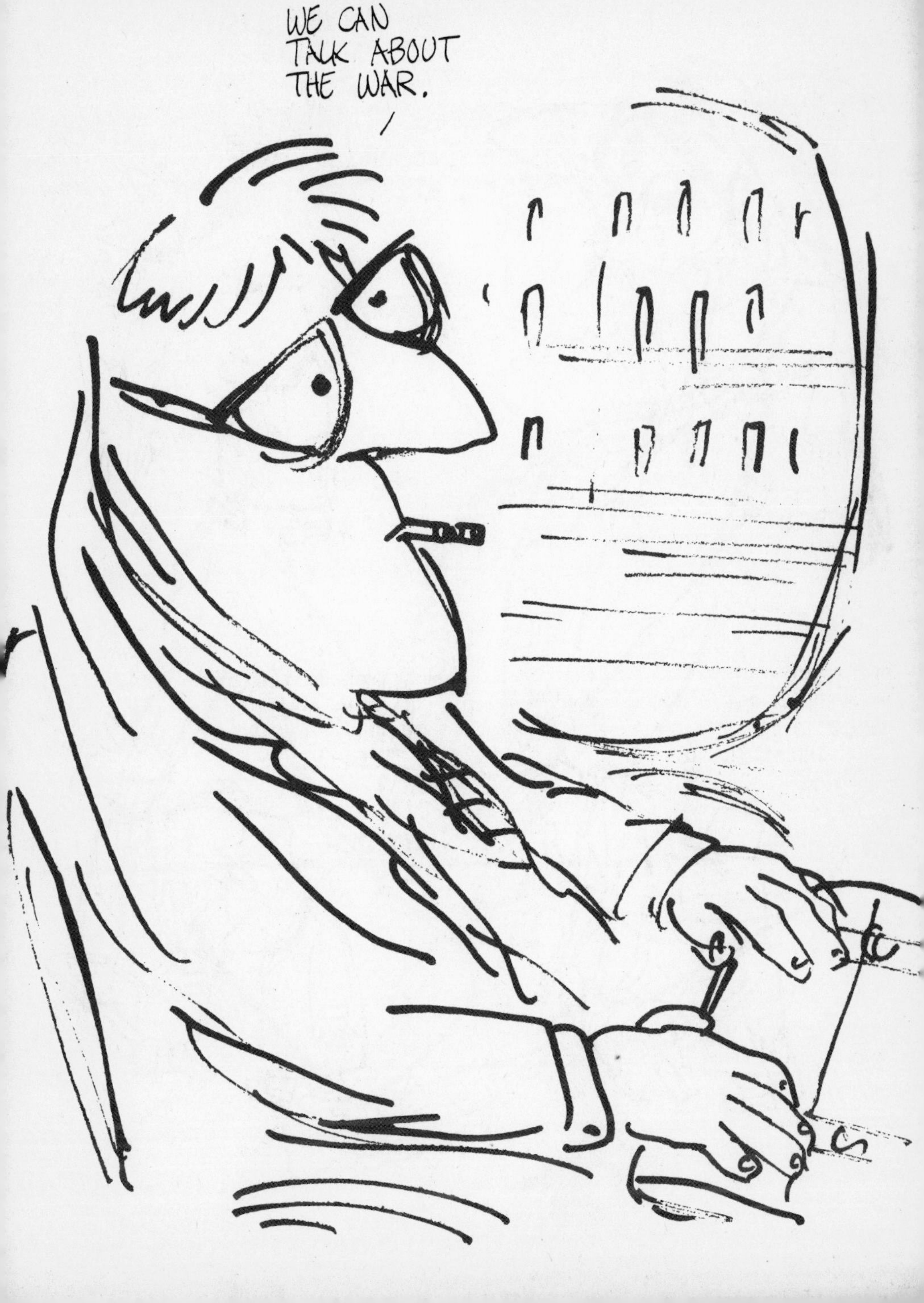
WE CAN TALK ABOUT THE WAR.

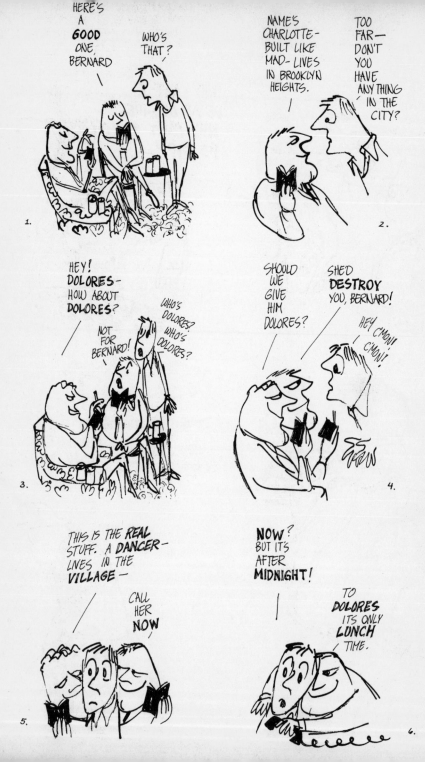

DON'T USE MY NAME.

HELLO—AM I SPEAKING TO DOLORES?

7.

WELL MY NAME IS BERNARD AND I WAS IN THE NEIGHBORHOOD AND A MUTUAL FRIEND SUGGESTED I CALL YOU. WHY DON'T I PICK UP SOME BEER AND DROP OVER FOR A WHILE?

8.

SHE SAID YES

9.

IT'S AFTER **MIDNIGHT** AND SHE'S GOING TO SEE **ME!** **SHE'S GOING TO SEE ME!**

10.

11.

HOW CAN YOU HAVE ANY RESPECT FOR SOMEONE LIKE THAT?

THINK IT'LL
SNOW IN TIME
FOR CHRISTMAS?

YEARS AND YEARS AND YEARS AGO WHEN
THERE WERE WOLVES IN WALES – WHEN
WE SANG AND WALLOWED IN CAVES THAT
SMELT LIKE SUNDAY AFTERNOONS IN DAMP
FRONT FARMHOUSE PARLORS, IT
SNOWED AND SNOWED.

THERE WERE PRESENTS THEN —
BAGS OF MOIST AND MANY COLORED
JELLY BABIES, HARDBOILEDS,
TOFFEE, FUDGE AND ALLSORTS
AND TROOPS OF BRIGHT TIN
SOLDIERS WHO IF THEY COULD
NOT FIGHT - COULD ALWAYS RUN —

YEAH,
BUT.

NOT MANY THOSE MORNINGS
TROD THE PILING STREETS.
IN THE RICH AND HEAVY
AFTERNOON, THE UNCLES
BREATHING LIKE DOLPHINS
AND THE SNOW DESCEND-
ING, I WOULD SIT AMONG
FESTOONS AND NIBBLE
DATES.

ALL
I
ASKED
WAS—

FOR DINNER WE HAD TURKEY
AND BLAZING PUDDING—AND
AFTER DINNER THERE WAS
MUSIC—A COUSIN SANG
"CHERRY RIPE" AND ANOTHER
SANG "DRAKE'S DRUM".

THE SILENT ONE CLOUDED
HEAVENS DRIFTED ON TO
THE SEA AND THEN I
WENT TO BED.

with apologies to Dylan Thomas

1.

2.

3.

4.

5.

6.

7.

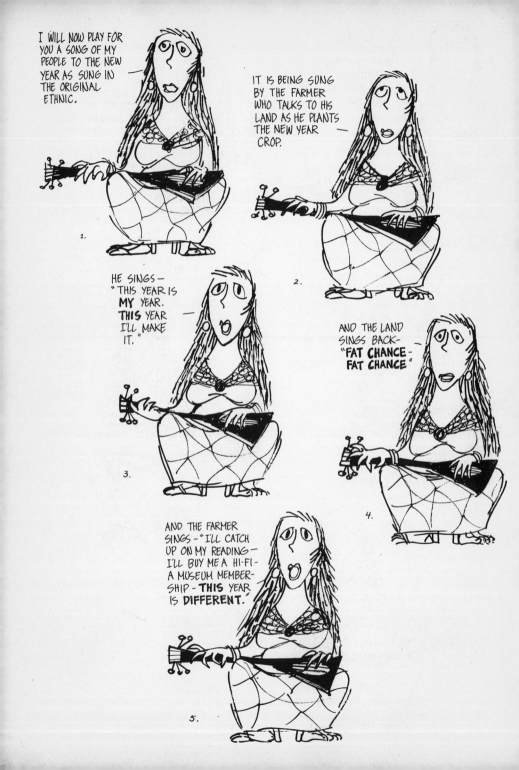

AND THE LAND
SINGS BACK—
"**WHO ARE YOU
KIDDING?
WHO ARE YOU
KIDDING?**"

6.

AND THE FARMER
SINGS—" I'LL
BE **CREATIVE**—
I'LL START ON
THAT **NOVEL**—
CERAMICS AND
JEWELRY— I'LL
HAVE **FULFILL-
MENT**"

7.

AND THE LAND
SINGS BACK—
"CUT OUT THE
NONSENSE.
WHY DON'T YOU
GROW UP.
YOU'LL FEED
ME **FOREVER.**"

8.

THEN THERE
IS A WILD
CIRCLE
DANCE
DONE ON
THE KNEES.

9.

IN MY
COUNTRY
IT CAN
GO ON
FOR YEARS.

plink plink
plink

10.

GOD — IT'S AN EN**TIRE**LY DIFFERENT CROWD THIS YEAR.

GOD — I FEEL LIKE A **STRANGER**

GOD — HOW I HATE TO BE **FIRST**. WHEN IS BOBO COMING UP?

BOBO IS OFF IN EUROPE.

1.

2.

GOD — I'LL **MISS** BOBO! WHAT TIME DO RICK AND GIGI GET HERE?

RICK AND GIGI **SPLIT** UP. HADN'T YOU HEARD?

GOD — WHAT CAN YOU **DEPEND** ON THESE DAYS? WHAT ABOUT RONNIE, SKIP AND BINKY?

TOO BUS' ALL T BUSY

3.

4.

SO I'VE DECIDED TO MARRY SIDNEY.

1.

I TRIED TO BREAK OFF BUT HE'S SO PERSISTENT. HE SAID I WAS HIS LAST CHANCE. IT'S IMPORTANT TO A MARRIAGE TO KNOW YOU'RE DESIRED.

2.

HE'S REALLY FAR MORE SENSITIVE THAN MOST PEOPLE THINK. LIKE I WARNED HIM HOW COMPULSIVE I AM— BUT HE SAID I WAS HIS DARLING GIRL AND HE WOULDN'T LET ME TALK ABOUT MYSELF THAT WAY. OVERLOOKING FAULTS IS VERY IMPORTANT IN A MARRIAGE.

3.

AND HE READS A LOT, TOO. HE MAKES IT HIS BUSINESS TO GET THROUGH "THE NEW YORKER" EVERY WEEK. YOU JUST DON'T NOTICE IT BECAUSE HE NEVER TALKS.

4.

AND I EXPLAINED HOW **VITAL** THE DANCE IS IN MY LIFE AND HE'S SURE THAT AS SOON AS HE SEES ONE HE'LL **LOVE** IT. MUTUAL INTERESTS ARE VERY IMPORTANT IN A MARRIAGE.

5.

AND, OF COURSE, ONE CAN'T IGNORE THAT HE HAS A FINE FINANCIAL FUTURE. HIS FATHER PROMISED HIM A RAISE AFTER THE WEDDING.

6.

AND HE'S **NOT THE TYPE** TO BE **UNREASONABLE** ABOUT PHYSICAL DEMANDS.

7.

ONCE I GET USED TO HIM, OURS CAN BE A VERY RICH EXPERIENCE.

8.

TAKE A LOOK, CHARLIE —
75 FEET LONG —
500 H.P. — **300**
POUNDS OF CHROME-
PERFUMED EXHAUST —
AND SHE RIDES
LIKE A **DREAM** —
FAN*TAS TIC!*

1.

HERE SHE IS, CHARLIE —
16 MM. — SOUND ON FILM —
SELF BLIMPED
AUTO ADJUSTING
ANAMORPHIC ATTACHMENT
WITH A SWITCH BLADE
FOCUS — TAKES PICTURES
LIKE A **DREAM** —
FAN*TAS TIC!*

2.

OVER HERE, CHARLIE —
50 INCH — FULL COLOR —
MULTI-IMAGE PICTURE
TUBE WITH A
FLEXI-RESPONSE
CHANNEL SELECTOR —
WORKS LIKE
A **DREAM** —
FAN*TAS TIC!*

3.

TAKE A LOOK, CHARLIE —
6 ELECTRO — HYDRO
TWEETERS —
8 WALL TO WALL
WOOFERS — WITH A
1200 WATT PRE-AMP
STEREO OUTPUT — PLAYS
LIKE A **DREAM** —
FAN*TAS TIC!*

4.

AND HEAR THIS, CHARLIE —
I RECORD MY OWN
TAPES! JUST LISTEN —
FAN*TASTIC!*

CLICK

ROAR

5.

6.

THAT WAS AN
H-BOMB BLAST
RECORDED **RIGHT**
ON THE SPOT—
SOUNDS LIKE ITS
IN THE **ROOM**
DOESN'T IT?
FAN*TAS*TIC!

IT'S A
FULL
LIFE,
CHARLIE.

7.

8.

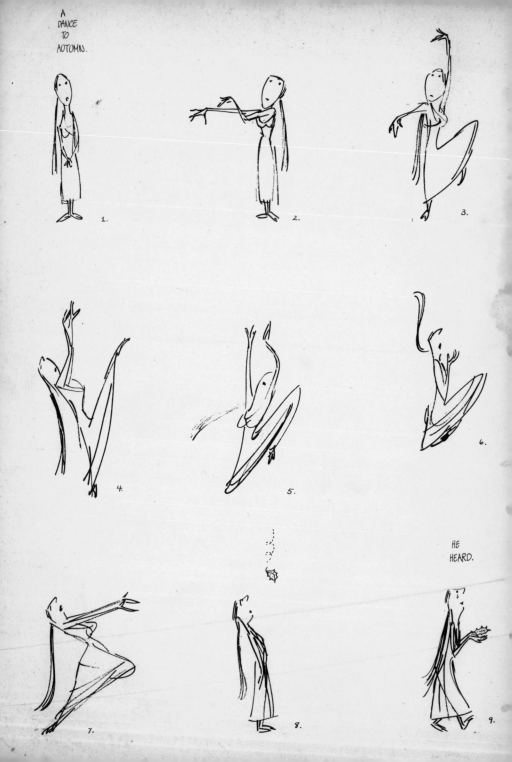

A
DANCE
TO
AUTUMN.

1.

2.

3.

4.

5.

6.

HE
HEARD.

7.

8.

9.